Back to Basics

MATHS

for 10–11 year olds

BOOK TWO

George Rodda

Difference and total

Attendance this week is **4732**.
Last week the
attendance was **3463**.

Total	Difference
4732	4732
+ 3463	− 3463
8195	1269

Check the total for the two weeks.
Check the difference for the two weeks.

Finish these additions.

1
```
  262
+₁143
  405
```

2
```
  302
+ 1 09
  411
```

3
```
  295
+₁ 95
  390
```

4
```
   79
+₁331
  410
```

5
```
  67
  23
+  9
  99
```

6
```
  53
  29
+ 13
  95
```

7
```
  49
  51
+ 10
 110
```

8
```
  39
  29
+ 49
 117
   2
```

Find the differences.

1
```
  2⁸90
−  89
  201
```

2
```
  3⁸9̸0
−  99
  291
```

3
```
  ³4̸07
−  78
  331
```

4
```
  ⁷8̸⁸8̸
−  99
  789
```

5   A school has 221 boys
    and 283 girls.

How many children are there
altogether? | 504 | children
How many more girls are
there than boys? | 62 | girls

```
283
221
 62
```

```
 221
−283
 39
```

```
 221
+283
 504
```

SMALL size: 250 tea bags

MEDIUM size: 500 tea bags

LARGE size: 1000 tea bags

Work out the total for:

1   1 large box
and 1 small box
     Total   1250   bags

2   1 large
1 medium
1 small
     Total   1750   bags

Find the difference in the number of bags.

3   1 large box
1 medium box
     Difference   500   bags

4   1 large box
1 small box
     Difference   750   bags

5   1 medium box
1 small box
     Difference   250   bags

6   2 large boxes
1 medium box
     Difference   1500   bags

7   2 medium boxes
3 small boxes
     Difference   250   bags

8   1 large box
2 medium boxes
     Difference   0   bags

Work these out.

1
$$
\begin{array}{r}
453 \\
138 \\
+\ 201 \\
\hline
792 \\
\end{array}
$$

2
$$
\begin{array}{r}
164 \\
237 \\
+\ 103 \\
\hline
504 \\
\end{array}
$$

3
$$
\begin{array}{r}
542 \\
-\ 243 \\
\hline
301 \\
\end{array}
$$

4
$$
\begin{array}{r}
1000 \\
-\ \ 99 \\
\hline
901 \\
\end{array}
$$

Find the total
and difference for
2735 and 3275.

5
$$
\begin{array}{r}
3275 \\
2735 \\
\hline
\end{array}
$$
Total   6010

6
$$
\begin{array}{r}
3275 \\
2735 \\
\hline
\end{array}
$$
Difference   1540

Multiplication

Each cart carries **15** passengers.

10 carts carry 15 x 10 = 150 people
 2 carts carry 15 x 2 =   30 people

12 carts carry 15
                x 12
                 30 (2 x 15)
                150 (10 x 15)
                180 people

Work these out.

1   15
        x 13
        45 (3 x 15)
        150 (10 x 15)
        195

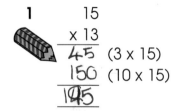

2   15
        x 14
        60 (4 x 15)
        150 (10 x 15)
        210.

Check the difference. $\boxed{210}$ – $\boxed{225}$ = 15

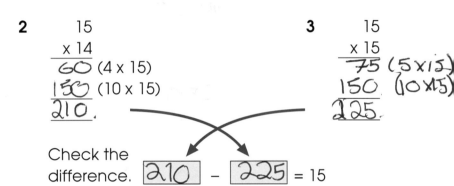

3   15
        x 15
        75 (5 x 15)
        150 (10 x 15)
        225.

4   150
        x 13
        450 (3 x 150)
        1500 (10 x 150)
        1950

5   150
        x 14
        600 (4 x 150)
        1500 (10 x 150)
        2100

Check the difference. $\boxed{2100}$ – $\boxed{1250}$ = 150

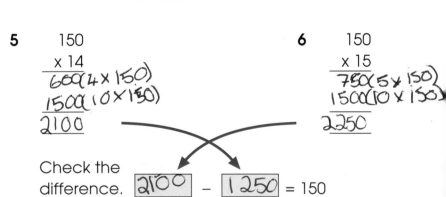

6   150
        x 15
        750 (5 x 150)
        1500 (10 x 150)
        2250

7   Potatoes cost 80p a kilogram (kilo).

10 kilos cost $\boxed{800}$ p = £ $\boxed{1 \cdot}$

 4 kilos cost $\boxed{320}$ p = £ $\boxed{3}$

14 kilos cost $\boxed{1120}$ p = £ $\boxed{11}$

4

Each pack contains 12 mints.

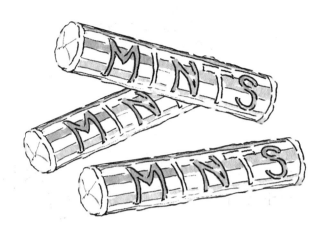

Work these out.

1   10 packs contain [120] mints
      5 packs contain [60] mints
      15 packs contain [180] mints
      15 x 12 = [180]

2   20 packs contain [240] mints
      4 packs contain [48] mints
      24 packs contain [288] mints
      24 x 12 = [288]

3   30 packs contain [360] mints
      2 packs contain [24] mints
      32 packs contain [384] mints
      32 x 12 = [384]

Work these out.

4   10 boxes hold [160] pens
      2 boxes hold [32] pens
      12 boxes hold [192] pens
      12 x 16 = [192]

5   20 boxes hold [320] pens
      3 boxes hold [48] pens
      23 boxes hold [368] pens
      23 x 16 = [368]

6   30 boxes hold [480] pens
      2 boxes hold [32] pens
      32 boxes hold [512] pens
      32 x 16 = [513]

Check your answers with a calculator.

Work these out.

1	**2**	**3**	**4**
12	12	50	51
x 11	x 12	x 12	x 12
132	144	600	612

Division

12 pieces, remainder 6 cm

10)126
120
6

This seaside rock is **126 cm** long. It is ready to be cut into pieces **10 cm** long.

Check: 12 x 10 = 120
120 + 6 = 126

Work these out to see how many pieces can be cut from different lengths.

1 0 1 3
10)130 cm

2 0 1 4
10)140 cm

3 0 1 6
10)160 cm

4 0 2 0
10)200 cm

5 0 1 3 rem 2
10)132 cm
130
2

6 0 1 6 rem 4
10)164 cm

7 0 1 9 rem 6
10)196 cm

New lengths are to be cut into 12 cm pieces.
Work these out.

1 0 0 9
12)108 cm

2 0 1 0
12)120 cm

3 0 1 2
12)144 cm

4 0 1 5
12)180 cm

5 0 0 rem
12)100 cm

0 0
12)100

6 0 0 rem
12)110 cm

7 ___ rem
12)138 cm

Check your answers with a calculator.

Fill in the answers.

1 110 ÷ 10

= [ ]

2 115 ÷ 10

= [ ] rem [ ]

3 111 ÷ 10

= [ ] rem [ ]

4 200 ÷ 20

= [ ]

5 220 ÷ 20

= [ ]

6 245 ÷ 20

= [ ] rem [ ]

Work out these divisions.

1

19)209

2

21)231

3

21)252

4

50)250

5

19)210 rem [ ]

6

19)208 rem [ ]

7

18)200 rem [ ]

Don't forget to check your answers.

```
      12 cm
15)180 cm
```

Check: 15 x 12
      =180

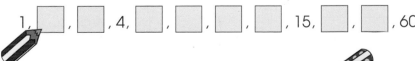

15 children are going to share a length of rock which is **180 cm** long.

1 Does 15 divide exactly into 180? [ ]

2 What length does each child receive? [ ] cm

3 15 divides **exactly** into 60, so 15 is called a **divisor** of 60.

```
    4
15) 60
```

Write down the other divisors of 60.

1, [ ] , [ ] , 4, [ ] , [ ] , [ ] , [ ] , 15, [ ] , [ ] , 60

4 Use a calculator to divide 12321 by 111. [ ]

Graphs

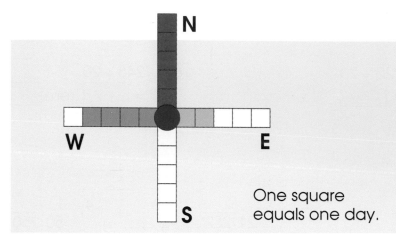

W
E
N
S

One square equals one day.

This graph shows how many times the wind blew and from which direction it blew.

The wind direction was recorded for 20 days.

1 Fill in this table from the graph.

Wind from the	N	S	E	W
Number of days			2	

2 Out of the 20 days, how many were windy?

3 On how many days was there no wind?

Finish this graph showing the direction from which the wind came.

4 From which direction did the wind come most?

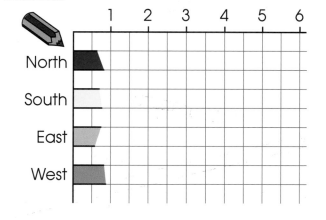

	1	2	3	4	5	6

North
South
East
West

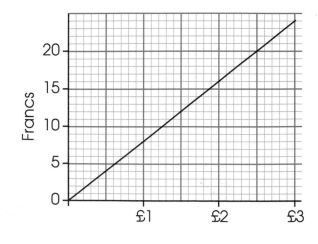

Francs

20

15

10

5

0

£1   £2   £3

This is a graph showing that 8 francs = £1.

Use the graph to help you fill in the answers.

1 £2 = ___ francs

2 50p = ___ francs

3 £1.50 = ☐ francs

4 £1.75 = ☐ francs

5 £2.50 = ☐ francs

6 12 francs = £☐

7 6 francs = ☐ p

8 18 francs = £☐

Draw a graph showing the average daily sunshine for each of these towns.

Town	Hours
Roughsea	4
Seahaven	6.5
Brightsea	9
Downcliffe	7.5
Sandy Bay	8

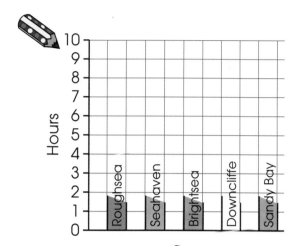

1 Which town had the least sunshine? ☐

2 Which town had the most sunshine? ☐

3 What was the total sunshine for the 5 towns? ☐

4 The average for the 5 towns is ☐ ÷ 5 = ☐ hours

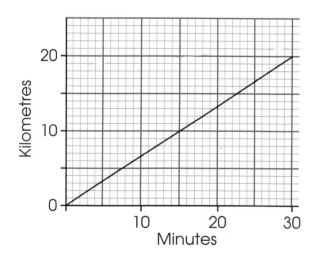

This graph shows the distance travelled by a kangaroo at a speed of 40km per hour.

Use the graph to help you fill in these answers.

1 In 30 minutes he hops ☐ km.

2 In 15 minutes he hops ☐ km.

3 He should hop 6km in ☐ minutes.

4 He should hop 5km in ☐ minutes.

Problems

The signs are missing from these sums.
Put the right sign in: +, −, x or ÷, to make them correct.

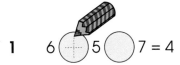

1 6 (÷) 5 ( ) 7 = 4

2 6 ( ) 5 ( ) 7 = 8

3 2 ( ) 3 ( ) 1 = 4

4 2 ( ) 3 ( ) 1 = 7

5 10 ( ) 10 ( ) 2 = 98

6 10 ( ) 10 ( ) 2 = 200

7 50 ( ) 49 = 1

8 50 ( ) 49 = 1 rem 1

9 55 ( ) 5 ( ) 9 = 99

10 50 ( ) 10 ( ) 5 = 25

Water freezes at 0°C on this thermometer. Use the thermometer to help you fill in the tables.

1

Temperature	0°	+5°	+5°	+4°	−5°
Rise	5°	5°	10°	7°	10°
New temperature	°	°	°	°	°

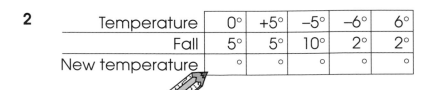

2

Temperature	0°	+5°	−5°	−6°	6°
Fall	5°	5°	10°	2°	2°
New temperature	°	°	°	°	°

This is a list of waist measurements for 8 children.

| 62 | 59 | 60 | 58 | 60 | 63 | 64 | 62 | cm |

1   Which is the shortest measure? [   ] cm

2   Which is the longest measure? [   ] cm

3   Add up the 8 measures. [   ] cm

Divide your answer by 8. [   ] cm

The average waist size is [   ] cm

4   How many of the 8 waist sizes are below average? [   ]

5   How many of the sizes are above average? [   ]

Fill in the time and the digital time underneath each clock.

1

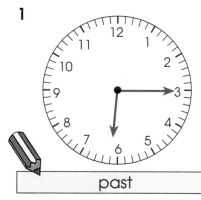

past

  ○ :

2

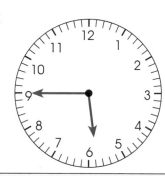

[   ]

[:   ]

3

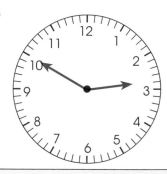

[   ]

[:   ]

A 1p coin weighs 3.6g.
A 2p coin weighs 7.2g.

Write down the weight of

1   100 (1p) coins [   ] g

2   50 (2p) coins [   ] g

3   150 (1p) coins [   ] g

4   150 (2p) coins [   ] g

Tenths and hundredths

35p = £0.35

42p = £0.42

p		£
35		0.35
+ 42	or	+ 0.42
77p		£0.77

Use this scale to help you answer these sums.

1 2.2 + 0.9 = ☐   **2** 6.8 – 0.5 = ☐   **3** 5.2 + 1.7 = ☐

4 4.5 + 1.6 = ☐   **5** 4.5 – 1.6 = ☐   **6** 7.2 – 1.9 = ☐

Change these fractions to decimals.

1 $\frac{7}{10}$ = 0.☐   **2** $\frac{7}{100}$ = 0.☐   **3** $\frac{5}{10}$ = 0.☐

4 $1\frac{5}{10}$ = ☐   **5** $1\frac{5}{100}$ = ☐   **6** $10\frac{1}{10}$ = ☐

Change these decimals to fractions.

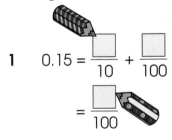

1 $0.15 = \frac{☐}{10} + \frac{☐}{100}$

$= \frac{☐}{100}$

2 $0.34 = \frac{☐}{10} + \frac{☐}{100}$

$= \frac{☐}{100}$

3 $0.25 = \frac{☐}{10} + \frac{☐}{100}$

$= \frac{☐}{100} = \frac{☐}{4}$

4 $0.75 = \frac{☐}{10} + \frac{☐}{100}$

$= \frac{☐}{100} = \frac{☐}{4}$

Work these out.

1	3.75 + 1.06	2	2.75 + 3.31	3	2.56 + 1.45	4	7.93 + 3.08
5	5.75 − 1.26	6	7.63 −1.72	7	8.46 − 2.47	8	9.98 − 1.99
9	1.2 x 6	10	1.25 x 6	11	5.05 x 9	12	5.55 x 8

13 3)3.63   14 3)4.53   15 4)8.12   16 4)9.24

Remember that 1m = 100cm and 1cm = 10mm.

Fill in the answers.

1   0.5cm = ☐/10 cm = ☐ mm   2   0.8cm = ☐ mm

3   0.4cm = ☐ mm   4   1.4cm = ☐ mm   5   2.4cm = ☐ mm

6   0.05m = ☐/100 m = ☐ cm   7   0.06m = ☐ cm

8   0.5m = ☐ cm   9   0.6m = ☐ cm

Use your calculator to help you fill in **is greater than** or **is less than.**

1   4.75 ÷ 3   ☐   1.5.

2   4.75 ÷ 4   ☐   1.2.

3   999.99 ÷ 11   ☐   90.

Fractions

This graph shows the colour of cars for sale.

$\frac{1}{4}$ are red, $\frac{1}{2}$ are blue,

$\frac{1}{8}$ are grey, $\frac{1}{8}$ are green.

$\frac{1}{4} + \frac{1}{2} + \frac{1}{8} + \frac{1}{8}$

$= \frac{2}{8} + \frac{4}{8} + \frac{1}{8} + \frac{1}{8} = \frac{8}{8} = 1$

Use this chart to help you answer questions 1 to 11.

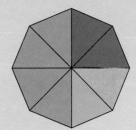

1 $\frac{1}{2} = \frac{\square}{10}$ **2** $\frac{2}{5} = \frac{\square}{10}$

$\frac{1}{2}$ S
$\frac{1}{4}$ S
$\frac{1}{8}$ S
$\frac{1}{3}$ S
$\frac{1}{5}$ S
$\frac{1}{10}$ S

Write the sign
> "is more than"
< "is less than"

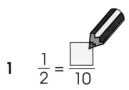

3 $\frac{1}{4} \square \frac{1}{2}$ **4** $\frac{1}{4} \square \frac{1}{3}$ **5** $\frac{3}{4} \square \frac{2}{3}$

6 $\frac{4}{5} \square \frac{1}{2}$ **7** $\frac{4}{5} \square \frac{3}{4}$ **8** $\frac{3}{4} \square \frac{7}{10}$

9 $\frac{3}{8} \square \frac{3}{10}$ **10** $\frac{3}{8} \square \frac{2}{5}$ **11** $\frac{7}{8} \square \frac{3}{4}$

Work out these additions and subtractions.

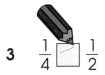

1 $\frac{3}{5} + \frac{2}{5} = \square$ **2** $1\frac{3}{4} + \frac{1}{4} = \square$ **3** $1 - \frac{3}{8} = \frac{\square}{\square}$

4 $\frac{1}{2} + \frac{3}{8} = \frac{7}{\square}$ **5** $\frac{1}{2} - \frac{3}{8} = \frac{\square}{\square}$ **6** $\frac{7}{10} + \frac{1}{5} = \frac{\square}{\square}$

7 $\frac{7}{10} - \frac{1}{5} = \frac{\square}{\square}$ **8** $\frac{2}{5} + \frac{1}{10} = \frac{\square}{\square}$ **9** $\frac{2}{5} - \frac{1}{10} = \frac{\square}{\square}$

10 $\dfrac{7}{10} + \dfrac{9}{10} = \dfrac{\Box}{\Box}$ **11** $\dfrac{7}{10} + \dfrac{1}{5} = \dfrac{\Box}{\Box}$ **12** $\dfrac{3}{4} + \dfrac{7}{8} = \dfrac{\Box}{\Box}$

Fill in the answers.

1 $1\dfrac{1}{2} \times 2 = \Box$ **2** $\dfrac{1}{4} \times 4 = \Box$ **3** $\dfrac{3}{4} \times 4 = \Box$

4 $1\dfrac{2}{5} \times 2 = \dfrac{\Box}{\Box}$ **5** $\dfrac{3}{5} \times 2 = \dfrac{\Box}{\Box}$ **6** $\dfrac{4}{5} \times 2 = \dfrac{\Box}{\Box}$

7 $\dfrac{1}{5}$ of $20 = \Box$ **8** $\dfrac{1}{4}$ of $20 = \Box$ **9** $\dfrac{1}{2}$ of $72 = \Box$

10 $\dfrac{1}{2}$ of $\dfrac{2}{3} = \dfrac{\Box}{\Box}$ **11** $\dfrac{1}{2}$ of $\dfrac{1}{2} = \dfrac{\Box}{\Box}$ **12** $\dfrac{1}{2}$ of $\dfrac{1}{5} = \dfrac{\Box}{\Box}$

Work these out.

1   L. Driver sells 12 of his 36 cars.

What fraction has he sold? $\dfrac{\Box}{}$

What fraction has he left? $\dfrac{\Box}{}$

2

L. Driver's petrol tank holds 80 litres of petrol.

When $\dfrac{1}{2}$ full he will have $\boxed{}$ litres.

When $\dfrac{1}{4}$ full he will have $\boxed{}$ litres.

When $\dfrac{3}{4}$ full he will have $\boxed{}$ litres.

3

These 4 oil cans hold 1 litre each.

How many $\dfrac{1}{2}$s in 4? $\boxed{}$

How many $\dfrac{1}{4}$s in 4? $\boxed{}$

How many $\dfrac{1}{10}$s in 4? $\boxed{}$

Shapes and co-ordinates

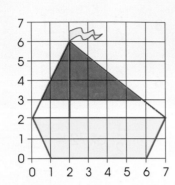

Check that the boat's flag is at the point (2,6).

Check that the ends of the deck are (0,2) and (7,2).

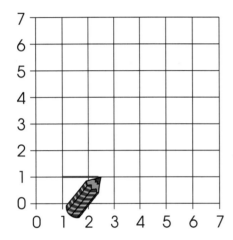

1 With a red pencil and ruler join
(1,1) → (5,1) → (5,5) → (1,5) → (1,1).

The shape drawn is a

2 With a blue pencil and ruler join
(3,3) → (3,5) → (0,5) → (0,3) → (3,3).

The shape drawn is a

3 Join (0,0) → (4,0) → (4,4) → (0,4) → (0,0).
The shape drawn is a

4 Join (5,6) → (2,6) → (2,0) → (5,6).
The shape drawn is a

5 Which point makes a rectangle with
(0,0), (0,5) and (6,5)?   (☐ , ☐)

6 Which point makes a square with
(1,1), (1,6) and (6,6)?   (☐ , ☐)

7 Which point makes a letter T with
(1,6), (1,5), (3,5), (3,2), (4,5), (6,5), (6,6)?   (☐ , ☐)

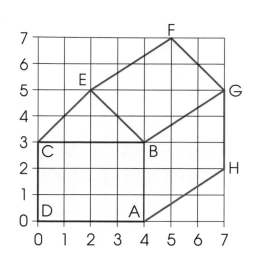

This is a diagram of Sam's bicycle shed.

1 Write down the co-ordinates of the points:

A (☐ , ☐)   B (☐ , ☐)

C (☐ , ☐)   D (☐ , ☐)

E (☐ , ☐)   F (☐ , ☐)

G (☐ , ☐)   H (☐ , ☐)

2 What is the shape A, B, C, D?

3 Does shape A, B, G, H have four right angles on the diagram? ☐

What shape will A, B, G, H be on the real shed? _____

4 Here is a message in code. Each co-ordinate represents a letter.

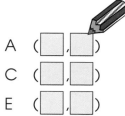

Change the co-ordinates to letters and read the message.

(1,3) (2,2) (1,1) (1,3) | (3,3) (3,1) (1,2) | (3,2) (2,2) (2,1)

☐ ☐ ☐ ☐ | ☐ ☐ ☐ | ☐ ☐ ☐

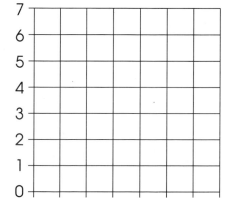

Use this grid to make the first letter of your name.

Write down the co-ordinates you use.

My initial is

(☐ , ☐) (☐ , ☐) (☐ , ☐) . . . . . .

Angles and degrees

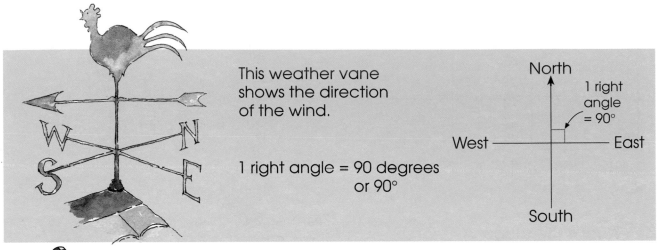

This weather vane shows the direction of the wind.

1 right angle = 90 degrees
or 90°

North

1 right angle = 90°

West —————— East

South

1

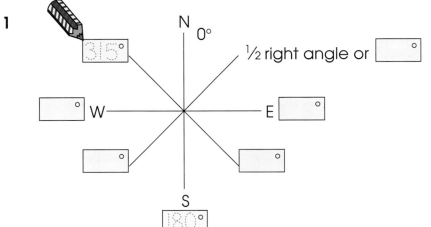

N 0°

315°

½ right angle or ☐°

W ———— [°]

E [°]

☐° ☐°

S 180°

Fill in the missing numbers on this compass.

2 Change these fractions of right angles to degrees.

Right angles	½	1	1½	2	3	4
Degrees	°	°	°	°	°	°

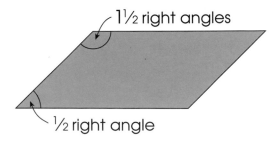

1½ right angles

½ right angle

3 How many right angles are there in this rectangle?

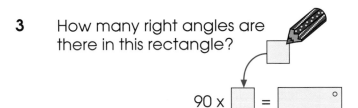

90 x ☐ = [°]

4 How many right angles make up the angles of this rhombus?

90 x ☐ = [°]

18

5

Draw an arrow to show the position of this hand when it turns:

A clockwise through 1 right angle (red);

B clockwise through 1½ right angles (blue);

C clockwise through 3 right angles (green);

D anti-clockwise through 3 right angles (yellow).

From A, B, C, D which 2 finish in the same position? ☐ and ☐

6

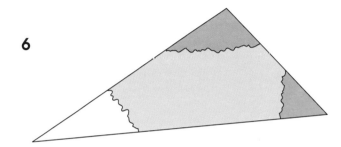

Cut out a triangle. Tear off the 3 corners and fit them together like this.

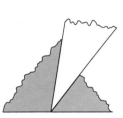

How many right angles do the 3 corners add up to?

☐ right angles or ☐ degrees.

Try again with another angle.

7 How many degrees will this sentry turn through if he:

Turns right? ☐°

Starts again and turns left? ☐°

Starts again and turns to look behind him? ☐°

Starts again and turns completely round? ☐°

Length and distance

This bridge is 1200 metres long.

1200 metres = 1200 x 100 cm
= 120000 cm

1200 metres = 1200 ÷ 1000 km
= 1.2 kilometres

1000 m = 1 km

Change these kilometres to metres.

1 2 km = ☐ m   **2** 2½ km = ☐ m   **3** 3.5 km = ☐ m

4 4.1 km = ☐ m   **5** 3.9 km = ☐ m   **6** ⅕ km = ☐ m

Change these metres to kilometres.

1 3000 m = ☐ km   **2** 2500 m = ☐ . ☐ km   **3** 4250 m = ☐ . ☐ km

1 m = 100 cm.

Change these metres to centimetres.

1 3 m = ☐ cm   **2** 2½ m = ☐ cm   **3** 0.5 m = ☐ cm

4 10 m = ☐ cm   **5** 2³⁄₁₀ m = ☐ cm   **6** 1⅕ m = ☐ cm

Change these centimetres to metres.

1 400 cm = ☐ m   **2** 450 cm = ☐ . ☐ m   **3** 360 cm = ☐ . ☐ m

4 365 cm = ☐ . ☐ m   **5** 420 cm = ☐ . ☐ m   **6** 205 cm = ☐ . ☐ m

7 Fill in the numbers. 1 km = ☐ metres

= ☐ centimetres

= ☐ millimetres

The baby giraffe's shadow is 3 times as long as Jenny's shadow.

Check this on the picture.

Fill in the missing numbers.

1 Jenny is 1m 50cm tall.
The giraffe will be

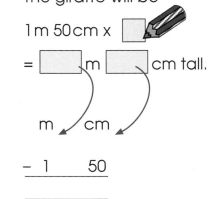

1m 50cm x ▢

= ▢ m ▢ cm tall.

```
      m     cm
 –    1     50
    _____
```

2 The difference in height between Jenny and the giraffe is

Work these out.

1
```
   km      m
    2     500
 + 3     500
 _____
```

2
```
   km      m
    4     750
 + 2     500
 _____
```

3
```
    m     cm
    1     75
 + 2     50
 _____
```

4
```
    m     cm
    2     50
 – 1     75
 _____
```

5
```
   km      m
    3     500
 x         4
 _____
```

6
```
    m     cm
    4     60
 x         5
 _____
```

7 1km ÷ 5 = ▢ metres

8 1 metre ÷ 5 = ▢ cm.

9 Sarah runs across the bridge. Fill in the distances.
1 crossing is 1200m or 1.2km.

2 crossings will be ▢ m or ▢ km

5 crossings will be ▢ m or ▢ km

Numbers

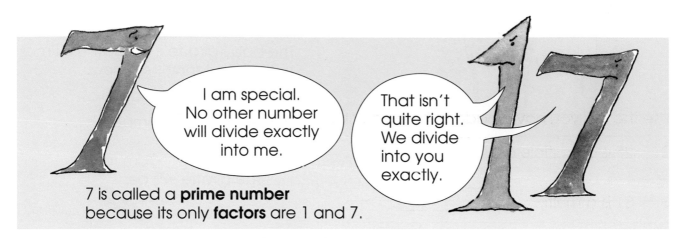

I am special. No other number will divide exactly into me.

That isn't quite right. We divide into you exactly.

7 is called a **prime number** because its only **factors** are 1 and 7.

1 The factors of 7 are 1 and

Fill in the **factors** for these numbers.

2

	Factors		
2	☐ , ☐		
3	☐ , ☐		
4	☐ , 2 , ☐		
5	☐ , ☐		
6	☐ , ☐ , ☐ , ☐		
7	☐ , ☐		
8	☐ , ☐ , ☐ , ☐		

3

	Factors					
9	☐ , ☐ , ☐					
10	☐ , ☐ , ☐ , ☐					
11	☐ , ☐					
12	☐ , ☐ , ☐ , ☐ , ☐ , ☐					
13	☐ , ☐					
14	☐ , ☐ , ☐ , ☐					
15	☐ , ☐ , ☐ , ☐					

4 Write a list of **prime numbers** in order.

2 , ☐ , ☐ , ☐ , ☐ , 13

5 Which is the only **even** prime number? ☐

10 is called a **multiple** of 2 because 2 divides exactly into 10.
Write in the missing numbers.

6 10 is a multiple of 1, 2, ☐ , 10.

7 12 is a multiple of 1, 2, ☐ , ☐ , ☐ , 12.

8 16 is a multiple of 1, ☐ , ☐ , ☐ , 16.

1 Find the factors of these numbers.

	Factors
19	
25	
31	
49	

	Factors
16	
23	
36	
91	

Use the lists you have made to help you fill in these missing numbers.

2   25 is a multiple of ⬚ .

3   31 is a multiple of ⬚ .

4   The prime numbers you have found are ⬚ .

5

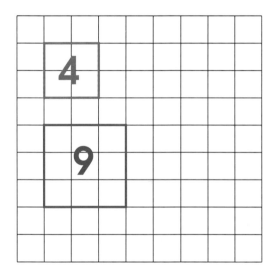

4 and **9** are called **square** numbers.

$2 \times 2 = \mathbf{4}$ $3 \times 3 = \mathbf{9}$

Work out the next four square numbers.

4, 9, ⬚ , ⬚ , ⬚ , ⬚

Is 100 a square number? ⬚

6   **3** and **6** are **triangular** numbers. Work out and draw the next two triangular numbers.

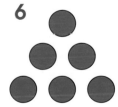

Average

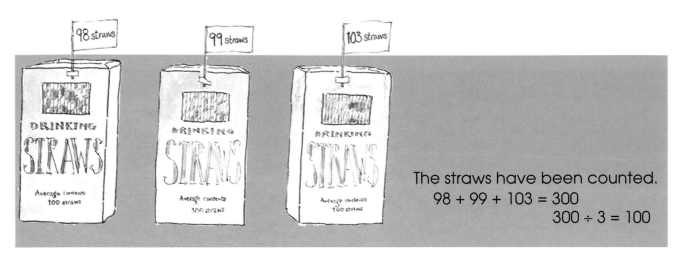

98 straws   99 straws   103 straws

The straws have been counted.
98 + 99 + 103 = 300
300 ÷ 3 = 100

Each box shows that the average numbers of straws is [   ] .

Is the average number for the 3 boxes 100? [   ]

1 How many straws should there be altogether in 10 boxes?

[   ] x 10 = [   ] straws

2 Fill in the missing numbers.

The total length of these 3 pieces of string is

[   ] + [   ] + [   ] = [   ] cm

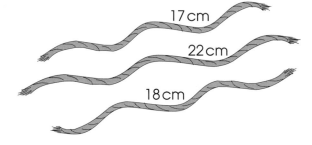

17 cm

22 cm

18 cm

The average length of the 3 pieces of string is [   ] ÷ 3 = [   ] cm

Find the average of these sets of numbers.

1 5, 7, 6
average [   ]

2 5, 6, 10
average [   ]

3 10, 20, 30
average [   ]

4 10, 20, 20, 50
average [   ]

5 2, 3, 4, 5, 6
average [   ]

6 4, 5, 6, 7, 8
average [   ]

7 2, 4, 6, 8, 10
average [   ]

8 1, 2, 3, 4
average [   ]

9 4, 8, 12, 16
average [   ]

1 Three bluebells have grown to the heights shown on this graph.

Fill in the numbers.

Total height for the 3 bluebells is:

6½ cm + ☐ cm + ☐ cm

= ☐ cm

Average height for the 3

= ☐ ÷ ☐ = ☐ cm.

Finish drawing the column to show the average height.

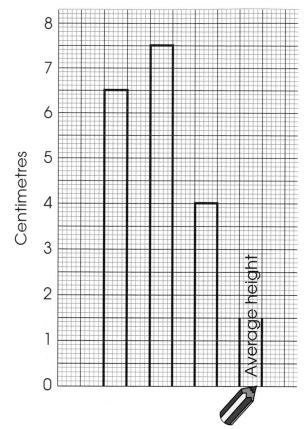

2 This table shows how much money was put in the box each day.

Day	Mon	Tue	Wed	Thur	Fri	Sat
Amount	£2	£3.50	£4.50	£5.00	£6.50	£8.50

For 6 days, how much money was put in altogether?

£ ☐

What was the average amount per day? £ ☐

3 This table shows the weights of 5 children.

Name	Angie	Ben	Chas	Debbie	Eric
Weight	56kg	45kg	55kg	54kg	40kg

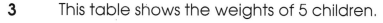

Work out:

The total weight. ☐ kg

The average weight. ☐ kg

How many children are more than the average weight? ☐

How many children are less than the average weight? ☐

Area and volume

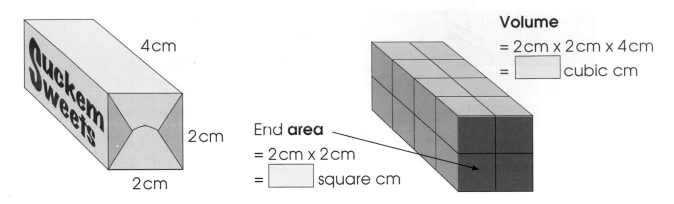

Volume

= 2cm x 2cm x 4cm

= ⬚ cubic cm

End **area**

= 2cm x 2cm

= ⬚ square cm

1 Finish working out: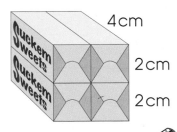

The end area = ⬚ square cm

The volume = ⬚ cubic cm

Work out the area of one side of the Suckem sweets pack.

2cm   **Suckem Sweets**   4cm

Area = ⬚ cm x ⬚ cm

= ⬚ square cm

Fill in the answers for these displays of sweets.

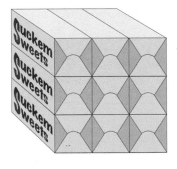

4cm

2cm

2cm

2 Number of packs = ⬚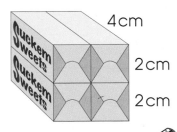

End area = ⬚ square cm

Volume = ⬚ cubic cm

3 Number of packs = ⬚

End area = ⬚ square cm

Volume = ⬚ cubic cm

4 Work out the volume of 8 packs of Suckem sweets. ⬚ cubic cm

5

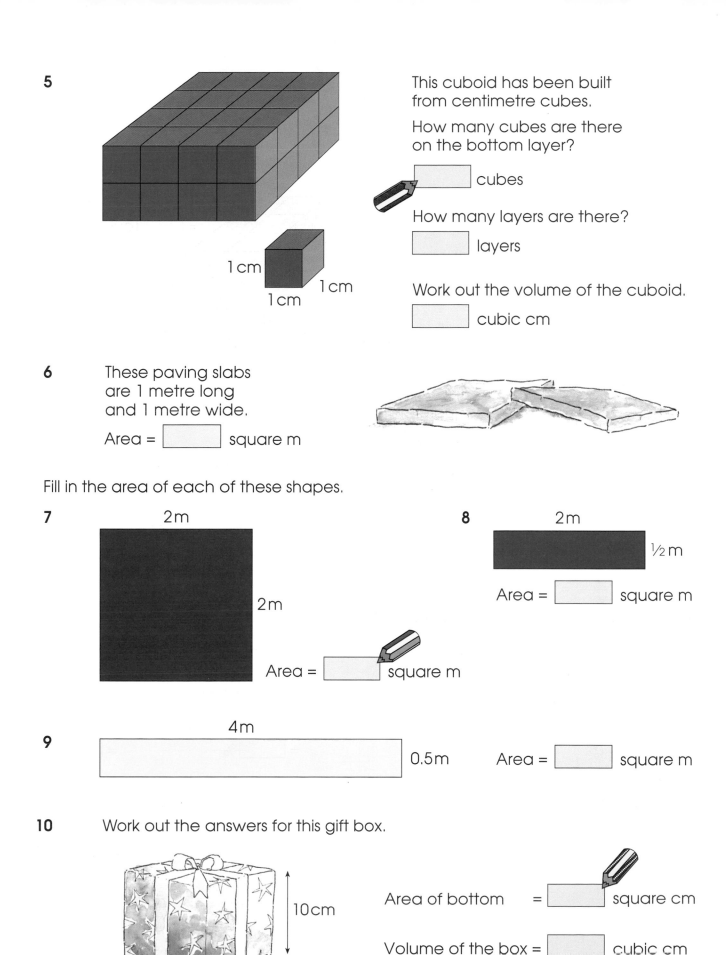

This cuboid has been built from centimetre cubes.

How many cubes are there on the bottom layer?

☐ cubes

How many layers are there?

☐ layers

Work out the volume of the cuboid.

☐ cubic cm

6 These paving slabs are 1 metre long and 1 metre wide.

Area = ☐ square m

Fill in the area of each of these shapes.

7

2m

2m

Area = ☐ square m

8

2m

½ m

Area = ☐ square m

9

4m

0.5m

Area = ☐ square m

10 Work out the answers for this gift box.

10cm

10cm   10cm

Area of bottom = ☐ square cm

Volume of the box = ☐ cubic cm

Percentage %

45   **30**   **25**

Tea

Coffee

Squash

100 people were asked which of these they preferred.

45 said tea
30 said coffee
25 said squash
———
100

Tea was chosen by $\frac{45}{100}$, or **45 per hundred**, or **45 per cent** (%).

Fill in the missing numbers.

Coffee was chosen by $\dfrac{\boxed{}}{100}$ = $\boxed{}$ per cent

Squash was chosen by $\dfrac{\boxed{}}{100}$ = $\boxed{}$ per cent

Change these fractions to per cent.

1 $\dfrac{7}{10}$ = $\dfrac{\boxed{}}{100}$ = $\boxed{}$ %

2 $\dfrac{9}{10}$ = $\dfrac{\boxed{}}{100}$ = $\boxed{}$ %

3 $\dfrac{1}{5}$ = $\dfrac{\boxed{}}{10}$ = $\dfrac{\boxed{}}{100}$ = $\boxed{}$ %

4 $\dfrac{2}{5}$ = $\dfrac{\boxed{}}{10}$ = $\dfrac{\boxed{}}{100}$ = $\boxed{}$ %

Change these decimals to per cent.

1   0.25   = $\boxed{}$ %

2   0.75   = $\boxed{}$ %

3   0.5   = $\boxed{}$ %

4   0.6   = $\boxed{}$ %

Change these percentages to fractions and to decimals.

1   50% = $\dfrac{\boxed{}}{\boxed{}}$ = $\boxed{0.}$

2   25% = $\dfrac{\boxed{}}{\boxed{}}$ = $\boxed{0.}$

3   30% = $\dfrac{\boxed{}}{\boxed{}}$ = $\boxed{0.}$

4   3% = $\dfrac{\boxed{}}{\boxed{}}$ = $\boxed{0.}$

5   60% = $\dfrac{\boxed{}}{\boxed{}}$ = $\boxed{0.}$

6   99% = $\dfrac{\boxed{}}{\boxed{}}$ = $\boxed{0.}$

Work out the answers.

1   50% of 200 = [   ]

2   25% of 200 = [   ]

3   75% of 200 = [   ]

4   20% of 100 = [   ]

5   40% of 100 = [   ]

6   60% of 100 = [   ]

7   There were 50 boxes of biscuits in this pile.

How many are left?

[   ] boxes

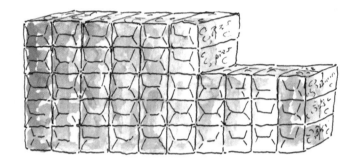

What fraction has been sold?

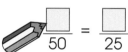 $\frac{\square}{50} = \frac{\square}{25}$

What fraction is left?

$\frac{\square}{50} = \frac{\square}{25}$

What % has been sold?

[   ] %

What % is left?

[   ] %

8

This box contains 25 biscuits. 12 are chocolate and the rest are plain.

Fill in this table.

Chocolate	12	$\frac{12}{25} = \frac{\square}{100}$	0.[ ]	[ ] %
Plain	[ ]	$\frac{\square}{25} = \frac{\square}{100}$	0.[ ]	[ ] %

If 10 biscuits have been eaten, what % is left?   [   ] %

Approximation

This music centre will cost £85.99 or about £86.

Think of **approximately** as meaning **about the same as** or **round about**.

1 Round these numbers to the nearest **unit**.

	1.9	1.4	4.7	5.1	6.09	3.19	11.7
Is about		1					

2 Round these numbers to the nearest **ten**.

	29	42	50.9	67	76	94	95.1
Is about							

3 Round these numbers to the nearest **hundred**.

	102	98	198	149	109	560	431
Is about							

4 Round these numbers to the nearest **pound**.

	£0.99	£1.01	£2.60	£2.06	£2.66	£4.75	£3.25
Is about	£	£	£	£	£	£	£

5 Round these lengths to the nearest **centimetre**.

	2.1cm	11mm	19mm	4.7cm	101mm	99mm	96mm
Is about	cm	cm	cm	cm	cm	cm	cm

1   Fill in this table by **approximating** the answer
    and then working out the **exact** answer.

	Is about	Answer
18 x 9	20 x 10 = 200	162
21 x 9		
39 x 5		
43 x 8		
59 x 11		

2   Round these distances to the nearest **metre**.

	99cm	95cm	105cm	140cm	599cm	6.4m	999cm
Is about	m	m	m	m	m	m	m

3   Round these weights to the nearest **kilogramme**.

	950g	1020g	3.9kg	3.1kg	$2\frac{1}{4}$kg	$2\frac{3}{4}$kg	9999g
Is about	kg	kg	kg	kg	kg	kg	kg

4   Anne's hand width is 9.5cm or about 10cm.

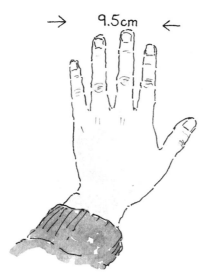

→   9.5cm   ←

Fill in this table.

Hands	1	2	3	4	5
About	10cm	cm	cm	cm	cm

Work out 9.5cm x 5 = ⬚ cm

Round your answer to
the nearest 10cm.   ⬚ cm

Answers

To Parents: We have not provided *all* the answers here. We suggest that items to be coloured in on squares. lengths and graphs should be checked by you. In the case of activities where calculations are performed by your child, it would be good practice to get him/her to use a calculator to check the answers.

page 2

1 405	2 411	3 390	4 410
5 99	6 95	7 110	8 117
1 201	2 291	3 329	4 789
5 504; 62			

page 3

1 1250	2 1750	3 500	4 750
5 250	6 1500	7 250	8 0
1 792	2 504	3 299	4 901
5 6010	6 540		

page 4

1 195	2 210	3 225	4 1950
5 2100	6 2250	7 800p = £8;	

320p = £3.20; 1120p = £11.20

page 5

1 120; 60; 180; 180	2 240; 48; 288; 288
3 360; 24; 384; 384	4 160; 32; 192; 192
5 320; 48; 368; 368	6 480; 32; 512; 512
1 132	2 144	3 600	4 612

page 6

1 13	2 14	3 16	4 20
5 13 rem 2	6 16 rem 4	7 19 rem 6	
1 9	2 10	3 12	4 15
5 8 rem 4	6 9 rem 2	7 11 rem 6	

page 7

1 11	2 11 rem 5	3 11 rem 1	4 10
5 11	6 12 rem 5		
1 11	2 11	3 12	4 5
5 11 rem 1	6 10 rem 18	7 11 rem 2	
1 Yes	2 12		
3 2, 3, 5, 6, 10, 12, 20, 30, 60		4 111	

page 8

1 5, 3, 4	2 14	3 6	4 North
1 16	2 4		

page 9

3 12	4 14	5 20	6 1.50	7 75	8 2.25
1 Roughsea	2 Brightsea	3 35	4 7		
1 20	2 10	3 9	4 7.5		

page 10

1 –	2 –, +	3 +, –	4 x, +
5 x, –	6 x, x	7 –	8 ÷
9 ÷, x	10 ÷, x		
1 5, 10, 15, 11, 5		2 –5, 0, –15, –8, 4	

page 11

1 58	2 64	3 488; 61; 61
4 4	5 4	
1 ¼ past 6; 06:15	2 ¼ to 6; 05:45	
3 10 to 3; 02:50		
1 360	2 360	3 540	4 1080

page 12

1 3.1	2 6.3	3 6.9	4 6.1
5 2.9	6 5.3		
1 0.7	2 0.07	3 0.5	4 1.5
5 1.05	6 10.1		
1 $^{15}/_{100}$	2 $^{34}/_{100}$	3 $^3/_4$	4 $^1/_4$

page 13

1 4.81	2 6.06	3 4.01	4 11.01
5 4.49	6 5.91	7 5.99	8 7.99
9 7.2	10 7.50	11 45.45	12 44.40
13 1.21	14 1.51	15 2.03	16 2.31
1 5	2 8	3 4	4 14
5 24	6 5	7 6	8 50
9 60			
1 greater	2 less	3 greater	

page 14

1 $^5/_{10}$	2 $^4/_{10}$	3 <	4 <	5 >	6 >
7 >	8 >	9 >	10 <	11 >	
1 1	2 2	3 $^5/_8$	4 $^7/_8$	5 $^1/_8$	
6 $^9/_{10}$	7 $^1/_2$	8 $^1/_2$	9 $^3/_{10}$		

page 15

10 $^{16}/_{10}$ or $1^3/_5$	11 $^9/_{10}$	12 $^{13}/_8$ or $1^5/_8$
1 3	2 1	3 3	4 $^{14}/_5$ or $2^4/_5$
5 $^6/_5$ or $1^1/_5$	6 $^8/_5$ or $1^3/_5$	7 4	8 5
9 36	10 $^1/_3$	11 $^1/_4$	12 $^1/_{10}$
1 $^{12}/_{36}$ or $^1/_3$; $^{24}/_{36}$ or $^2/_3$		2 40; 20; 60	
3 8; 16; 40			

page 16

1 square	2 rectangle	3 square
4 triangle	5 (6,0)	6 (6,1)
7 (4,2)		

page 17

1 A (4,0), B (4,3), C (0,3), D (0,0), E (2,5),	
F (5,7), G (7,5), H (7,2)	2 rectangle
3 No; rectangle	4 sums I are I fun

page 18

1 45; 90; 135; 225; 270
2 45; 90; 135; 180; 270; 360
3 360	4 360

page 19

5 A and D
6 2; 180
7 90; 90; 180; 360

page 20

1 2000	2 2500	3 3500	4 4100
5 3900	6 200		
1 3	2 2.5	3 4.25	
1 300	2 250	3 50	4 1000
5 230	6 120		
1 4	2 4.5	3 3.6	4 3.65
5 4.2	6 2.05		
7 1000; 100000; 1000000			

page 21

1 4m 50cm	2 3m	
1 6km	2 7km 250m	3 4m 25cm
4 75cm	5 14km	6 23m
7 200	8 20	
9 2400, 2.4; 6000, 6		

page 22

1 7	2 1, 2	3 1, 3, 9
	1, 3	1, 2, 5, 10
	1, 4	1, 11
	1, 5	1, 2, 3, 4, 6, 12
	1, 2, 3, 6	1, 13
	1, 7	1, 2, 7, 14
	1, 2, 4, 8	1, 3, 5, 15
4 3, 5, 7, 11	5 2	6 5
7 3, 4, 6	8 2, 4, 8	

page 23

1 1, 19	1, 2, 4, 8, 16
1, 5, 25	1, 23
1, 31	1, 2, 3, 4, 6, 9, 12, 18, 36
1, 7, 49	1, 7, 13, 91
2 1, 5, 25	3 1, 31	4 19, 23, 31
5 16, 25, 36, 49; Yes; (10 x 10)		
6 10	and 15	

page 24

1 1000	2 57; average 19			
1 6	2 7	3 20	4 25	5 4
6 6	7 6	8 2½	9 10	

page 25

1 18cm; average 6cm
2 £30; average £5
3 250kg; average 50kg; 3; 2

page 26

1 4; 16; 2 x 4 = 8	2 4; 16; 64
3 9; 36; 144	4 128

page 27

5 16; 2; 32	6 1	7 4
8 1	9 2	10 100; 1000

page 28

Coffee 30%; Squash 25%
1 70	2 90	3 20	4 40
1 25	2 75	3 50	4 60
1 ½ = 0.5	2 ¼ = 0.25	3 $^3/_{10}$ = 0.3
4 $^3/_{100}$ = 0.03	5 $^3/_5$ = 0.6	6 $^{99}/_{100}$ = 0.99

page 29

1 100	2 50	3 150	4 20	5 40	6 60
7 42 boxes, $^8/_{50}$ = $^4/_{25}$, 16% sold;					
$^{42}/_{50}$ = $^{21}/_{25}$, 84% left					

8		$^{48}/_{100}$	0.48	48%
	13	$^{13}/_{25}$ = $^{52}/_{100}$	0.52	52%	60% left

page 30

1 2, 5, 5, 6, 3, 12
2 30, 40, 50, 70, 80, 90, 100
3 100, 100, 200, 100, 100, 600, 400
4 1, 1, 3, 2, 3, 5, 3
5 2, 1, 2, 5, 10, 10, 10

page 31

1 20 x 10 = 200	189
40 x 5 = 200	195
40 x 10 = 400	344
60 x 10 = 600	649
2 1, 1, 1, 1, 6, 6, 10	3 1, 1, 4, 3, 2, 3, 10
4 20, 30 40, 50; 47.5cm; 50cm	

32